WORST© ENGINEERS

First published in Great Britain by Scribo MMXXI
Scribo, an imprint of
The Salariya Book Company
25 Marlborough Place, Brighton, BN1 1UB

ISBN 978-1-913971-13-7

Book design by David Salariya

Printed and bound in China

The text for this book is set in Century Schoolbook
The display type is Jacob Riley

www.salariya.com

Illustrations: Isobel Lundie

The Long-Lost Secret Diary of the World's Worst Engineers

Written by
Tim Collins

Illustrated by
Isobel Lundie

Chapter One

Paris, 1888

May 26th

Malik: I am beginning this top-secret diary so I can record my progress in the world of engineering. As if climbing some vast tower, I will rise higher and higher until I stand above all others. In this age of technology, I shall forge great metal marvels that will beckon us on to a new world.

An extraordinary top-secret project is beginning soon, and I shall be part of it, as will my twin sister Leila, who knows nothing about this diary. All I can state now is that it involves two of the greatest nations on Earth.

Leila: Malik, I have found your diary. It was inside your pillow case. If you really want to keep it secret, find somewhere better. Anyway, father bought this notebook, this pen and this ink for both of us, so I should be allowed to write here too.

And it should be about OUR rise to the top, not just yours.

May 27th

Malik: My sister discovered this diary last night. This is a worrying development. I was going to write more about our upcoming secret meeting, but I'll hold off for now. I'll wait and see if my next hiding place is breached too.

Leila: Found it again. I knew you'd put it inside your stocking drawer, because your eyes kept darting there when I questioned you about it last night. Anyway, there's no need to hide it anymore because I've spoken to father and he agrees that all this stuff belongs to both of us.

For once in your life, I think you've had a good idea. We should be documenting what is happening. When you've been taken on as an apprentice by Monsieur Gustave Eiffel, the greatest engineer in the world, you really should record all the things he teaches you.

And yes, I have just written his name down. Stop trying to pretend everything is secret.

May 28th

Malik: I've just had a conversation with father, and it appears that I must share this diary with my sister. But her handwriting is slightly different from mine, so if you're reading this in the future, you'll know which parts to ignore. I myself shall not be reading what she adds.

Leila has already revealed that we're working with the famous Monsieur Eiffel, so I ought to describe how this came to be.

Ten years ago, when we lived in Algiers, father's friend Hassan invited him to come over to Paris and work with him in Monsieur Eiffel's foundry in Levallois-Perret. Father accepted, only meaning to go for a year, so he could save some money and bring it home to us.

But Monsieur Eiffel was so impressed by father's commitment to his work that he offered him the job of clerk instead. Father excelled in the post and decided to stay, so then we all moved to Paris.

Leila and I were introduced to Monsieur Eiffel, and when we promised we could work just as hard as father, he agreed to take us on as apprentice engineers.

Whilst father works in the office on the bottom floor, we go and help out Monsieur Eiffel in his studio on the top floor.

Through Father's dedication, and Monsieur Eiffel's kindness, we have permanently left Algeria for a brilliant new life in France.

Leila: Brilliant? Father and mother don't exactly have perfect lives.

Father much prefers the office to the foundry, but it's still tough work. He's always exhausted by the time he walks us home. His fingers and forehead are covered in ink, and his shirt is drenched with sweat. He's getting dark rings around his eyes and a hunched back from all the time he spends scribbling in ledgers.

As for mother, I know she wishes we were back in Algeria, even if we have more money here. Father has bought her a black woollen dress and jacket, and a wide-brimmed hat and a white parasol, so she can look like the Parisian ladies, but she says the fabric is uncomfortable. She finds the markets near our house confusing, and complains that she can't get the right ingredients for her tajines.

But for Malik and I, things have been pretty good. Working with Monsieur Eiffel is a great opportunity, and we intend to make the most of it.

May 29th

Malik: The meeting took place today, and I can now reveal more about the project. The countries that it concerns are France and the United States of America.

We shall help to build a huge statue called 'Liberty Enlightening the World' that will be given as a gift to the USA from France. It has been designed by the sculptor Frédéric Auguste Bartholdi, whom we met today.

Monsieur Eiffel led us to the garden of the Trocadéro Palace, where a huge copper female head was on display. The face was three metres wide and five metres tall, and was topped by a crown with seven spikes jutting out. We later learned that these spikes are meant to represent the seven continents and seven oceans. Enough of the neck and shoulders had also been built to show that the statue will be wearing a long, flowing robe.

This is just a part of Bartholdi's statue. When the whole thing is complete, it will look like Liberty, the Roman Goddess seen on the Great Seal of France.

As we approached the gigantic head, we could see a man with a thick beard and curly moustache. He turned out to be Bartholdi, and he launched straight into a speech about how important his statue was.

At one point, he fell still, and I thought he was finally going to introduce himself properly. But he thrust one hand into the air and held the other next to his chest to show us the position of the statue.

After twenty minutes of singing the praises of his giant Lady Liberty, he finally revealed exactly what he wanted us to do. We need to design a strong framework that will go inside the statue.

It's going to be placed on Bedloe's Island in New York Harbour. So everyone who sails into that great city will see this wonderful symbol of freedom and remember their friends in France. But it won't be much of a gift if it keels straight over into the sea, which is why he's come to the best three engineers in France for help.

`Leila: What Malik wrote is pretty much right. Except for the bit about France's three best engineers. He was asking Eiffel for his help, not us. He probably didn't even notice we were there. Malik also failed to mention that we went inside the head itself, climbed a spiral staircase, and looked` out of the windows in the crown. I mean, a diary is a place where you note down unusual things from the day, isn't it? You'd think going inside a giant head would be worth mentioning.

GET REAL

'Liberty Enlightening the World' is a 46-metre-high copper statue built on an island in New York Harbour. The idea for the statue came from the politician Édouard de Laboulaye, and it was designed by the sculptor Frédéric Auguste Bartholdi. It is better known as the Statue of Liberty.

May 30th

Malik: This is such an honour. Monsieur Eiffel is giving us a chance to design the inside of the statue whilst he mulls the problem over. He busied himself in the corner of his studio today with his pencils and measuring instruments. But he gave us a box of wooden sticks and glue, and said that he would use one of our ideas if it was better than his.

Imagine if he picks mine. This statue will be a new landmark, to rank alongside the Pyramids of Egypt and the Colosseum in Rome. I shall be remembered forever if I'm the one who works out how to keep it standing.

I worked all day, barely taking my eyes off my work. By the time we left, I had just completed my third attempt. I'm confident that Mr Eiffel will be impressed with it.

Leila: Hmm. Malik reckons that he barely took his eyes off his work. Yet he must have done at some point, because how else could he have copied my idea? I saw his first two attempts, and there was no way that they'd have been chosen. He was fixing the sticks into squares, even though everybody knows they're really weak shapes. I was sticking them in diagonal patterns to create triangles, which are much better at bearing weight.

After his two failed attempts with the squares, Malik glanced over and started on a new model that looked exactly like mine. I tried to take mine to the other side of the studio so he couldn't copy me anymore, but the bottom fell off and it took me ages to mend it. If Monsieur Eiffel chooses his design, I'm going to insist I get the credit.

GET REAL

Triangles are commonly used in engineering because they're rigid shapes. Engineers want to build structures that can survive strong forces, and triangles are good at distributing force. They have been used in everything from ancient pyramids to modern geodesic domes.

May 31st

Malik: Monsieur Eiffel was scribbling away in his studio when we arrived this morning, and I wondered if he'd been there all night. Eventually, he took a step back from his drawings, ran his hands down his greying moustache and beard, and announced that he was satisfied with his work.

We rushed over with our models, and asked him to examine them.

Or at least examine what was left of them. Leila had designed her model so poorly that when she placed it down on his desk, it collapsed, and she had to frantically apologise and sweep the shards of wood from his important diagrams.

There was a slight problem with my model as well, so Monsieur Eiffel rejected our ideas and showed us his. He'd covered dozens of pages with mechanical drawings and intricate calculations. He'd proved mathematically that each part of his design could bear the weight it needed to, before declaring it sound.

The idea he settled on was a four-legged iron pylon, with a strong supporting beam for the outstretched arm, carried over to the opposite side for counterbalance. Every sheet of copper making up the statue will be attached to the skeleton by an iron strap, so they rely on the central framework rather than each other.

We all agreed that Eiffel had come up with the best idea, and that we should present it to Monsieur Bartholdi.

Leila: Yes, it's true that my model collapsed as soon as I put it on Monsieur Eiffel's desk. But that was only because I damaged it when I moved it away from Malik yesterday. It didn't really matter anyway, because Malik completely stole my idea, so if his model had worked, mine definitely would have done, too.

But it didn't, which I can't help noticing that he forgot to mention. When he placed his model on the table, Monsieur Eiffel peered at it before putting a tiny metal weight on top of the outstretched arm.

The glue gave way, and the arm crumbled off.

Malik cringed and I pointed out that the statue wouldn't exactly be a great welcome to the USA if it dropped its massive copper torch on you as you sailed by.

Chapter 2

Helping or hindering?

June 1st

Malik: Father took us back home at noon for Friday prayers. He always went to the local mosque on Fridays when we lived in Algiers, and he insists that we keep up the tradition as best we can in France. Father vowed to raise us as Muslims when we left Algeria ten years ago, and he's stuck to it ever since.

Mother is always so happy when we return home. I think she loves doing something together as a family that doesn't involve Malik and I arguing about who's going to be the world's greatest engineer.

June 2nd

Malik: Monsieur Eiffel was working at his desk this afternoon when a strong gust of wind came in and blew his papers from it. I was helping him gather them up when he announced we were going for a walk.

He marched us up Montmartre Hill. The wind was still strong and he told us to hold our arms out and feel it blowing on us. He said if we wanted to become engineers, it was time for us to understand wind, our greatest enemy.

The blast of cool air didn't feel like much of an enemy after all that time in the stuffy studio. To better understand what Monsieur Eiffel was saying, I imagined that it was a gale blowing into New York in winter. I closed my eyes, lifted one hand in the air and pretended that I was Liberty herself.

I told myself the wind was trying to destroy me, and that I hated it.

Now I get it... I think!

When I opened my eyes, I could see that Monsieur Eiffel was nodding, impressed by my concentration. My sister, on the other hand, was smirking. I'm sure she'll add something below about how ridiculous I was being.

Leila: Ahem. I thought you weren't reading my entries, Malik? So why does it matter what I write?

As a matter of fact, I found your Lady Liberty impression quite convincing, and I'm sure there's a job for you on Bedloe's Island if Monsieur Bartholdi runs out of money for the real thing.

But rather than convincing myself I was an ancient Roman goddess, I was listening to Monsieur Eiffel. He didn't just take us up the hill to show us what wind was, as if we didn't already know. He was explaining how he takes the wind into account on each project.

In the case of the statue, he's designed the skeleton so it can move very slightly in high winds, which will stop the copper plates from cracking apart.

He told us about how much he loves iron, and how modern manufacturing processes mean we can make more of it than ever before. With the right skill and understanding, he said we can now 'use the magic of iron to defeat the tyranny of wind'.

Next time keep your ears open, Malik, even if you're going to close your eyes and imagine yourself towering over New York.

June 3rd

Malik: Monsieur Bartholdi came to the studio to look at our plans today, and he was delighted with them. He told us to go ahead with the framework and iron straps, and announced that he planned to construct the whole statue in his courtyard off the Rue de Chazelles, before dismantling it and sending it across the sea.

When Bartholdi had gone, Monsieur Eiffel explained that we'd need to work fast to get the framework finished on time. He usually sends rough diagrams and measurements to the drawing office on the first floor, which is overseen by Monsieur Koechlin. The diagrams they produce are then given to Armand, who is in charge of the foundry.

He'll do that with the main framework, but in the meantime, he's going to let us draw the iron straps from his notes, and then take them to Armand. When they're finished, we'll bring them up here for him to check, and then carry them over to Monsieur Bartholdi's workshop.

He spent two hours this afternoon teaching us how to make detailed diagrams of the straps that Armand and his team can work from. Tomorrow it will be time to put our skills to the test on the real job.

Leila: I'm ready, I think. This will be the biggest statue ever made, and if we make any mistakes it will slow the whole project down. So no pressure, then.

June 4th

Malik: Monsieur Eiffel was hunched over his desk working when we arrived. He'd already produced a large pile of drawings, and he handed half to me and half to Leila.

I sat on the far end of Monsieur Eiffel's desk and sifted through the ones I had to draw. It was hard to make out some of his notes, but I didn't want to interrupt his work.

I saw him glance over at my diagrams a few times, however, and I'm sure he would have said something if they weren't right.

Leila chose to sit at the table on the far side of the studio, by the door, so she could have been doing it completely wrong for all we knew.

I finished my batch first, and quickly ran across the courtyard to give them to Armand.

The heat of the foundry hit me as soon as I entered. Workers were collecting ladles of bright molten iron from the forge, and hurrying over to casts. As they poured them in, orange sparks flew into the air, and steam hissed around the large space.

The sound of the workers yelling and clanging their tools was deafening, and the tangy stench of hot metal and sweat made me wince.

I was worried about venturing too far into the room in case I accidentally stood in a bucket of liquid iron or something.

Luckily, Armand spotted me and came over. He grabbed the sheets and grumbled about how complicated the job was.

I told him we were part of one of the greatest engineering projects in history, and we should count ourselves privileged. He told me to try slaving away over a forge for fourteen hours a day and then tell him how privileged I felt.

Leila: I won't add much today. My hands are tired from all the drawing, and my eyes are strained from squinting at Monsieur Eiffel's handwriting. I didn't get through my pile as quickly as Malik, but I'm pretty sure I did an accurate job, which is all that matters to me.

June 5th

Malik: I returned to the foundry this morning to collect the iron straps from Armand, but all he handed over were a few tiny scraps that were about the size of bolts.

I asked what was going on and he brought my drawings over. I flicked through them, trying to find the part where I'd requested miniature straps. Then I saw it. I'd accidentally copied out the lengths in centimetres instead of metres.

I felt cold, despite the heat wafting over from the furnace. I stared at my drawings in horror, as it sunk in that I'd wasted a day of everyone's precious time. This wasn't good. But maybe it wouldn't matter if Monsieur Eiffel never found out about it.

I told Armand he'd done well, and that I'd be back with more diagrams very shortly. Then I ran back up to the studio and changed all the measurements to metres. I shuffled the papers so Armand wouldn't realise he'd already seen them, and went back down.

Armand complained about getting more work, but didn't seem to notice he was seeing the same things again.

Monsieur Eiffel was so distracted by his work that he didn't ask if any of the straps were ready yet, so I think I got away with it.

Leila: None of this would have happened if Malik had asked me to look over his drawings, of course. I put all my measurements in metres, partly because I actually checked my work, and partly because this is going to be the tallest statue ever built, and not a garden ornament. Imagine the disappointment on the faces of the Americans if we sent over a ridiculously tiny statue for their giant plinth.

June 6th

Malik: I took the new batch of iron straps to Monsieur Eiffel this afternoon. He examined them, before nodding and returning to his work. It looks like I'm off the hook, but from now on we must both give even greater focus to this important job. We can't afford another mistake.

Leila: What's this about both of us? I haven't done anything wrong!

June 7th

Malik: Another mistake was made today, but this time not by me. Leila delivered her diagrams to Armand early this morning. I collected the straps late this afternoon and took them back up to Monsieur Eiffel.

He was measuring one when he took a step back and squealed as though the iron was still hot. I asked him what was wrong and he said it was meant to have a hole halfway along so it could be fixed to the skeleton. He was about to stomp out to shout at Armand, but Leila grabbed the iron strap and said she'd take it back herself.

She emerged a few minutes later, saying that Armand was very sorry and had promised never to do it again. This didn't sound like something that Armand would say, so I was instantly suspicious.

I have been questioning my sister about what really happened, but she has revealed nothing.

Perhaps I'll make an exception and read her next diary entry to find out.

Leila: Alright, then. When I was taking the drawings over this morning, a cloud of dust blew up from the courtyard and made me sneeze. I know this is quite disgusting, but I didn't have time to cover my nose, and the sneeze went all over the diagram on top of my pile. I wiped it off, and I must have accidentally wiped the iron strap's hole away at the same time.

We've both made mistakes. Let's put it behind us and make sure we get things right from now on.

June 8th

Malik: My sister made a mistake yesterday that could have jeopardised the whole project if Monsieur Eiffel had not spotted it. His calculations are so precise that just one faulty strap could topple the statue, and bring his reputation down with it. I shall have to explain what happened to Monsieur Eiffel and suggest that he leaves all the drawing to me now.

Leila: If you tell him about my sneeze, I'll tell him about your minuscule straps.

June 9th

Malik: Unfortunately, Monsieur Eiffel no longer wants us to help him in the studio. Following a discussion about the sneeze and the measurement mix-up, he has decided it would be simpler if he sent everything through the drawing office instead.

Leila: What did you expect? We ended up having a huge row in front of him when all he wanted was peace. None of this would ever have happened if you'd just kept quiet.

June 10th

Malik: We both apologised to Monsieur Eiffel and asked if there was anything else we could do to help. He sent us over to Monsieur Bartholdi's workshop to check the measurements on the statue's copper plates. He told us to work separately and compare our results afterwards to make sure that there were no mistakes.

We walked over to Rue de Chazelles, and it wasn't hard to find the workshop, as huge piles of wooden scaffolding planks were lining the path to a courtyard. We stepped into it and could see three giant sheds with sloping roofs and wide entrances. I asked a workman where we could find Monsieur Bartholdi, and he pointed us to the one on our right.

We entered the cavernous space. Rows of workers were tapping metal and carving wood behind long tables. Ladders led to overhead walkways, where spare tools and planks were lined against the walls. And in a space at the back, there was a giant copper hand and torch.

I should have been looking around the workshop for Monsieur Bartholdi, but I couldn't take my eyes off the hand and torch. This was going to be the very top of the statue, even higher than the head. It would be the beacon that drew the huddled masses into New York.

I heard someone next to me muttering, 'magnificent', and turned to see Monsieur Bartholdi, admiring his own work with his hands planted on his hips. He said that this segment of the statue had already been all the way across the sea for display in Philadelphia and New York. Now it was back in France in time for the construction of the rest of Lady Liberty.

I told him we'd been sent to measure the copper plates, and he showed us into another of the workshops, where five curved sections – which looked like part of the left arm and sleeve – were leaning against some scaffolding.

We got to work on the sections, measuring each curve and fold as precisely as we could.

Leila: Malik is right that the completed part was amazing to see. It was as if a giant buried deep under the ground had thrust its hand through the floor. I'm not sure if Monsieur Eiffel hasn't just given us a task to keep us busy, but I don't mind if I get to see things like that.

GET REAL

The right hand and torch was the first section of the Statue of Liberty to be completed. It was shipped across the ocean to be displayed at the Philadelphia Centennial Exhibition, and then moved to Madison Square in New York. Visitors paid to climb the steps inside, and the money was put towards building the statue's base on Bedloe's Island.

June 11th

Malik: At lunchtime today, we sat in the courtyard, eating our bread and cheese, and watched the workers lug scaffolding around.

Monsieur Bartholdi came over to speak to us, and he was still enthusing about the statue. He's spent the last few years drumming up support and funding for it at home and in the USA, but he's lost none of his passion for it.

He told us about his epic quest to get Americans to give money towards the building of the plinth in New York. A newspaper man from New York called Joseph Pulitzer promised to print the name of everyone who donated, even if it was just a few cents. The public got behind his campaign, and he raised over $100,000.

Monsieur Bartholdi had to stop and wipe tears from his eyes as he described the ordinary citizens who'd skipped meals to make his dream a reality. It brought it home to me what an important project this is, and how hard we must work on it.

Leila: Monsieur Bartholdi loves copper every bit as much as Monsieur Eiffel loves iron. He told me all about how it can be beaten and bent without cracking, and how it eventually develops a protective green film on its smooth surface.

It's funny. I never pictured Lady Liberty being green as she greets arrivals to the USA. It will make her look as seasick as all the people finishing their long boat journeys, especially with that stern expression on her face. At least she isn't bending over and doing a giant copper spew into the Atlantic, I suppose.

I was about to ask Monsieur Bartholdi why the face of the statue looked so serious and fearsome when he mentioned that he'd based it on his own mother. Phew! Glad I avoided that awkward conversation.

June 12th

Malik: Monsieur Bartholdi showed us into the third workshop today so that we could measure two of the newest pieces. The floor was covered in tiny wood shavings and the air was thick with dust. I heard my sister sneezing, luckily not on any diagrams this time.

I couldn't make out much of what he was saying over the loud banging that filled the room, but Monsieur Bartholdi was trying to tell us how they'd made the panels. They'd started off with huge plaster sections, and then fitted intricate wooden moulds around them. Now the workers were hammering the copper sheets into the moulds. I could see three curved sections that would make up the shoulder being formed ahead of us.

A man to our right was working a drill into one of the plates to make the holes for the rivets.

A high screeching noise was added to the low pounding and my ears started to ache.

Leila: It was truly impressive to see all the effort that went into each plate, but I'm glad I don't have to work in that place every day. I couldn't concentrate on my measuring through all that noise, and had to keep starting over.

GET REAL

Frédéric Auguste Bartholdi chose copper because thin pieces could be hammered into shape, meaning the Statue of Liberty would be very light for its size. Even so, a huge amount of copper was needed, and much of it came from a mine in Visnes, Norway.

June 13th

Malik: We returned to Monsieur Eiffel with our measurements, and he looked through them. I asked him what he wanted us to do next, but he was concentrating too hard to hear me.

I thought I'd take my chance to get us a more important role, so I suggested that we could design some of the iron straps too. I said it would be great for us to get some practical experience on such a high-profile project.

He looked up from our notes and said practical experience was a brilliant idea. When he was starting out, he spent many days helping in foundries so he could see iron being melted and shaped. That gave him a real understanding of the metal he'd spent his life working with. He said we should report to Armand for work first thing in the morning.

Leila: Nice work, genius. Now we have to go and work in that hellhole. And for how long? Until the statue is completely finished?

Father says we should beg Monsieur Eiffel to reconsider. He told us about the stifling heat, and the backbreaking effort of carrying the heavy molten iron around.

He said he didn't know what sort of deeper understanding of iron we'd get anyway. He worked there for two years and all he learned was that it's very heavy and very dangerous.

Then mother said she was worried about me being in such a dangerous place, and I should stay at home with her and learn to look after the house instead. Beating rugs and scrubbing steps sounds even worse than being stuck in that scorching foundry.

Chapter 3

A new idea

June 14th

Malik: Armand frowned and grumbled when I told him we'd been sent to help him. You'd think he'd appreciate the extra staff after all that complaining about his workload.

The furnace hadn't yet been lit, so he said that I could practise handling the equipment before they got started.

I strode over and grabbed the long handle of the ladle. I tried to lift it, just as I'd seen the workers do, but it wouldn't budge. If it was this heavy without the iron in, what would it be like when it was full?

I strained as hard as I could, and managed to get the ladle a few centimetres off the ground. I just had to get it over to the cast and mime pouring some iron in, and Armand would see that I was fit to work for him.

I staggered forward with my arms shaking. I took one step and then another, fixing my eyes on the cast and telling myself I could make it.

Unfortunately, I was focusing so much that I didn't see a pair of plyers that had been left on the floor. I tripped over them and crashed down. The ladle clanged next to me and tipped over. If it had been full of molten iron, it would have covered me and turned me into a girder.

Armand snatched the ladle back and told me he didn't want our help, and even if he did, we'd only survive one day, so we'd make no difference to his workload.

This time I've written the full truth about my mishap, so Leila can't criticise and gloat when she's adding her comments tonight.

Leila: I wasn't going to criticise or gloat, Malik. I couldn't have been happier with your trial run. Partly because it was hilarious, and partly because it means we won't have to work in that horrible foundry, and we can ask Monsieur Eiffel for something else to do. Anything's got to be better than that.

June 15th

Malik: We had to go back to Monsieur Eiffel today and admit that Armand didn't want our help. Having failed at something as simple as helping out in the foundry, I was worried he would tell us it might be better if we found someone else to work for.

Monsieur Eiffel stared at us in silence for a moment, then said that we could probably get just as much understanding of iron from holding it as making it, so we should carry the finished iron straps over to Monsieur Bartholdi's workshop.

He sent us over today with two of the straps and a series of diagrams to show Monsieur Bartholdi exactly where they all went. I made sure my sister carried the diagrams and I took the straps, so I could get the best understanding of the metal.

Leila: I was happy to let my brother carry the straps so I could take the much lighter diagrams. I don't see what magical engineering lessons the straps are going to give us anyway. I think Monsieur Eiffel is just keeping us busy so we don't annoy him.

June 16th

Malik: We made three more trips today. With every journey, I could feel my love of iron growing. It really feels like I'm on course to become a true master of the material, like Monsieur Eiffel.

Leila: Well I'm learning nothing from lugging the lengths of iron around, but at least it means we're out on the streets rather than stuck inside. If you're going to live in the greatest city on Earth, you might as well see some of it.

Our route from Monsieur Eiffel's studio to Monsieur Bartholdi's workshop takes us down busy streets where horses pull carriages past gentlemen in smart jackets and tall hats, women in long, neat dresses holding parasols to shield themselves from the sun, and dusty children grasping sticks and pretending to fight Prussians.

We pass bistros serving fish, beef and vegetables. The rich, tangy smells of sauces and soups drift by, making me long for a day when I'm old enough to go and eat in those places whenever I feel like it.

We can hear laughter, arguments, the clopping of hooves and the shouts of busy workers trying to get through.

I could wander around the city all day, just watching it. I wish there was a way of seeing the whole place at once.

June 17th

Malik: We did four trips today. My appreciation of iron is growing all the time.

Leila: I'm sure we could have carried two iron strips each and made just two journeys. In fact, Monsieur Eiffel could just have put everything we've carried so far into a cart and brought it in one journey. It's a pointless task, and I'm going to confront him about it tomorrow.

June 18th

Malik: My sister stormed into the studio this morning and told Monsieur Eiffel how she felt. He was clearly in the middle of a difficult calculation, because he ignored her. She repeated herself, and Monsieur Eiffel turned away from his work and pushed his grey hair back with his palm. He scowled at her and I thought he was going to fire us both. I made it clear that I would be happy to stay on if he wanted to get rid of her.

Fortunately, he didn't want to get rid of us, and my sister's actions turned out to be rather wise for once.

Leila: Monsieur Eiffel came up with a suggestion that was much better than lugging iron straps around.

He said we should leave him to get on with the statue, but we could come up with ideas about what his next project should be.

His involvement with the statue will make him famous around the world, and his next project could be the one that cements his reputation. But what should it be?

He said we should spend the next few weeks coming up with ideas that will amaze the public, but are also practically possible and genuinely useful. We should draw diagrams of each one to show how it can be built.

When he's finished the statue, he'll look over our ideas and then pick the best one.

This is more like it. Finally, we're going to make a proper start to our engineering careers. See what happens when we speak up for ourselves, Malik?

June 19th

Malik: We spent today sitting at the back table of the studio, working in our notebooks and trying not to disturb Monsieur Eiffel.

It was actually really hard to think of a brilliant idea out of nowhere. If someone asked me to build a bridge across a valley I could visit it, stroke my chin, make some calculations and come up with a solution. But I spent most of today staring at a blank page.

Leila: Malik's right. It's hard to pull great engineering ideas out of your head. After a day of doodling on the paper, the only thing I came up with was a Liberty Statue holding two flaming torches instead of one. It wasn't the most original idea ever.

June 20th

Malik: I've done it. I've come up with an idea worthy of Eiffel's name. I spent today thinking about why everyone loves railways and bridges so much. It's because they help them to get to other places quickly. And what would get them there even faster? Wings.

It's so simple, and yet so brilliant. I'll design a set of iron wings that can fit onto everyone's arms. And when they flap them, they'll be able to fly as gracefully as a bird.

I haven't quite worked out the maths yet, but hopefully people will be able to take off from the ground if they move them really fast. Soon busy workers will no longer have to shout at crowds to get out of the way. They'll be able to gracefully fly over them instead.

But even if that doesn't work, I'm sure they could jump off something high and keep flying if they flap fast enough.

Two days in, and I've already got an idea that Monsieur Eiffel is bound to love.

June 21st

Leila: Okay, I've got something.

The steam hat.

Many gentlemen find their hats are too cold in winter, and too hot in summer. Now their headgear can work for them all year round, thanks to the miracle of technology.

A simple combustion engine that straps onto the wearer's back will produce enough power to open the top of their hat in summer at the pull of a lever. The air will circulate around their heads, cooling them down. The same engine will also send heat around their hat brims in winter.

And that isn't all. A second lever opens out a large umbrella attachment for rainy weather.

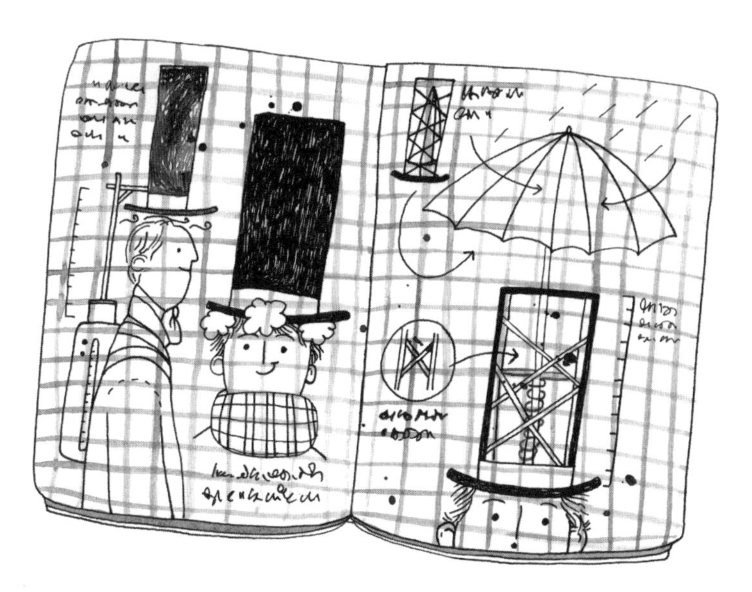

No need to ask what the weather is like anymore. With the steam hat, it doesn't matter.

June 22nd

Malik: I have just read my sister's idea and it's terrible. Who would walk around with a raging furnace on their back just so they can adjust their hat? Why not just take your hat off if you're too warm?

A cumbersome hat that will probably catch fire after a few hours is hardly a worthy follow-up to the Liberty Statue, is it?

June 23rd

Leila: You can sneer all you like, Malik. All the great inventions were dismissed at first. And whilst we're on the subject of safety concerns, why don't you climb onto the roof and test out your metal wings?

July 5th

Malik: We took a break from coming up with inventions today to see how the statue was coming along. The main framework has gone up now, and towers over the Rue de Chazelles from Monsieur Bartholdi's courtyard.

Men and women were stopping to gaze up at it, and coach drivers with flushed faces were yelling at them to step aside.

We walked into the alleyway, and a worker covered in plaster dust yelled at us to go away. When we reminded him that we worked for Monsieur Eiffel, he apologised and said they'd been getting a lot of trespassers since the pylon went up.

Inside the courtyard, there were men constructing scaffolding around the skeleton. I could see dozens of copper sheets leaning against their wooden moulds through the open doors of the workshop.

Even at this early stage, it's looking pretty spectacular. I can see why the Rue de Chazelles has suddenly found itself becoming a tourist spot.

Leila: If the workers are worried about the disruption the statue is causing now, what are things going to be like when it's finished? You can hardly tell people to move along because there's nothing to see when they're looking at one of the marvels of the modern world.

July 8th

Malik: Another great idea came to me today. We all love bridges that take us across rivers. But what if we thought about them in a different way?

Rather than using tonnes of iron to span the gap between each bank, what if we built a small platform that would run on rails set into the bed of the river? Levers at either end could move it along.

It would save on materials, and make it easier for ships to pass.

I have decided to call my invention 'Malik's Rolling Platform Bridge', and I have no doubt Monsieur Eiffel will be satisfied with it.

Leila: I wouldn't be so sure, Malik. Who would work the levers you mention? Would you have to employ people to operate them on both sides? Maybe it wouldn't be so much cheaper than a normal bridge after all.

July 9th

Leila: I've come up with a bridge idea that really does save on material. It's called 'Leila's Air Bridge'. It's a small flying capsule that you sit in, which is linked to a powerful, steam-driven mechanism.

You pull a lever and a giant piston catapults you across the river. The capsule is fitted with wings to ensure a smooth landing on the other side.

You step out, leaving the capsule free for someone else to use.

It's a great invention, and I've drawn some impressive diagrams of it. All I need to do now is work through the calculations.

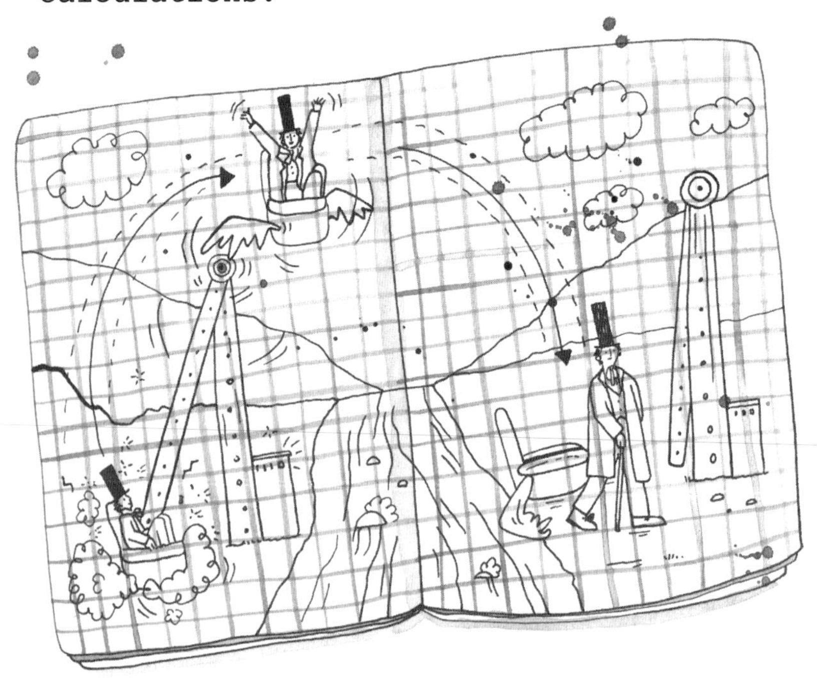

July 10th

Malik: Will these calculations explain how the capsule won't miss the opposite shore, plunging the user into the river and leaving them struggling to escape whilst the deadly contraption fills up with water? Because that's clearly what's going to happen.

July 15th

Malik: We went back to check on Lady Liberty today. As soon as we turned into the Rue de Chazelles, we could see a large crowd of men, women and children who were all gazing up over the buildings.

A strange half-statue was rising above them. The skeleton of its torso and raised arm was visible underneath thick wooden scaffolding.

The copper panels had already been added from the waist down, forming the flowing gown.

We weaved around the crowd and made our way into the alley. One of Monsieur Bartholdi's workers was standing guard to keep the curious out. He didn't recognise us, and at first he didn't believe we really knew Monsieur Bartholdi. But Leila did a convincing impression of Bartholdi talking about copper and waving his arms around, so he let us in.

We stood in front of the massive copper toes and gazed up at the incomplete statue. Red-faced workers were disappearing into the back and climbing up to fix new plates into place. Their clangs echoed inside the hollow structure.

We'd only meant to come for a few minutes, but ended up spending an hour gazing at the thing.

VINS
RETIF
HET

It's impossible to take your eyes off it.

Leila: I'm not surprised the workers were red-faced. The sun was hot today, and when I touched one of liberty's toes it felt like I'd dipped my finger into the ladle of molten iron. What must it be like working inside that thing? If the Americans don't want it, Monsieur Bartholdi could always use it as the world's biggest stove, and cook dinner for the whole city.

July 18th

Malik: I've just had my best idea yet. Monsieur Eiffel once told me about a tunnel that was made beneath the Thames in London using a 'tunnelling shield'. This is a scaffolding-like structure that protects workers from the sides caving in. They can use the shield to dig onwards, whilst others follow behind and build the tunnel walls from bricks.

Digging under a river using this device is all well and good, but imagine if you could tunnel under the ocean. La Manche, the stretch of sea connecting France and England, is just 34 kilometres long at its narrowest point. Building a tunnel beneath it, which we could call the 'Malik Tunnel', would make us famous throughout the world, and would be a truly worthy successor to the Liberty Statue.

As well as being an amazing idea, it's also totally practical, unlike exploding hats and catapult bridges.

We could even get Great Britain to do their share of the work by telling them to use a tunnelling shield of their own and meet us in the middle.

Leila: I hate to admit it, but you actually have a good idea there, Malik. I think I need to work harder on mine.

GET REAL

The Channel Tunnel, the rail tunnel linking England and France, finally opened in 1994. But plans for it can be traced all the way back to the early 19th century. One proposal was for a tunnel for horse-drawn carriages with an artificial island at the halfway point where passengers could change horses.

July 19th

Leila: I've come up with another one. We all love the steam locomotive and the pedal-powered cycle. But which is the greatest?

With the traincycle, you don't need to choose. Every seat comes with its own pedals, so the vehicle is propelled along by the people using it. It can even work on existing tracks, so there's no need to build new ones.

Passengers can travel just as they would on a normal locomotive, with the added benefit of exercise.
It also comes with a fair pricing system, so that the people who've paid the least agree to cycle hardest.

Imagine the thrill of seeing new places combined with the satisfaction of knowing it was your effort, or that of the poorer people around you, that got you there.

Malik: A small question about the traincycle, Leila. What happens if the people who agreed to pedal harder don't actually do it? Will the ones who paid more pull their weight to make up the difference? Or will the whole thing come to a halt whilst everyone argues until an actual steam train comes along and flattens anyone gullible enough to buy a ticket?

August 2nd

Malik: Lady Liberty is finally finished. We returned to Monsieur Bartholdi's courtyard today, this time with Monsieur Eiffel, who was carrying a huge wad of diagrams to send to the American builders.

Rue de Chazelles was jammed with spectators all the way down to Boulevard de Courcelles, and there was an atmosphere of carnival as everyone stared up at the statue.

A large man selling sugared water was doing good business with the hot crowd. He had a huge tin on his back that was covered with cups on hooks. A grubby boy stole one of his cups and he blundered after him like a confused bear.

One man was standing on a cardboard box and selling pamphlets about the history of the statue. I asked Monsieur Eiffel if we should buy one to see what he'd written about us. He replied that, given the cover was calling it a 'miraculous stone statue', it probably wasn't a trustworthy source.

Another man was selling misshapen lumps of iron that were meant to be models of the statue. Monsieur Eiffel scowled and pushed him aside. I couldn't tell if he was angry that the man was trying to make money from Monsieur Bartholdi's idea or if he was just offended by the terrible metalwork.

We got through to the courtyard and Monsieur Bartholdi rushed out, clapped Monsieur Eiffel on the back and thanked him for helping to bring his vision to life. He wiped away happy tears as he looked up at the huge face above us.

Monsieur Eiffel handed over his papers whilst barely taking his eyes off the statue. The two men carried out their meeting with their heads craned upwards. I expect we're all going to have neck ache tomorrow.

We took a final look at the statue before forcing our way back through the crowds. Tomorrow, Monsieur Bartholdi's workers will begin taking the huge structure apart again so they can ship it over to Bedloe's Island. And all the street vendors outside will have to find something else to make money from.

Leila: The statue looked truly amazing up close. I bet Monsieur Bartholdi regrets saying he'll give it away now, like when you buy someone such a good present that you decide to keep it for yourself after all.

I wish there was something as tall as the statue that could stay here forever. Imagine being able to look down on this beautiful city from such a great height!

Chapter 4

An Eiffel tower?

August 12th

Malik: We are showing our ideas to Monsieur Eiffel tomorrow. I spent today redrawing my best ones so they looked like proper mechanical diagrams. My sister, on the other hand, threw all her previous efforts in the bin. This wasn't just because she realised how bad they were, but because she's come up with a new one she thinks is much better.

Leila: The last thing I wrote yesterday made me realise what Monsieur Eiffel's next project should definitely be. I was thinking about how fantastic it would be to look down on Paris from a great height, and then it struck me. He should build a tower. Monsieur Eiffel is always talking about how iron is so strong it can bridge huge gaps in the landscape, but why don't we see how high off the ground it can get us?

I started with 100 metres, then increased the height to 200 metres, before settling on a 300-metre tower. That would be over three times taller than the Liberty Statue will be when it's on its base.

My tower wouldn't need to support any copper plates. It would just be an iron pylon rising into the sky to celebrate our age of technology.

As soon as I had this idea, I threw all my others in the bin. I knew straight away that The Leila Tower was the one. Monsieur Eiffel is bound to love it.

August 4th

Malik: This morning Monsieur Eiffel finished rolling up all his Liberty Statue diagrams, and was free to listen to our ideas.

I offered to go first. I stood in front of Monsieur Eiffel and went through my concepts. He wasn't very impressed by my iron wings, to put it mildly, and said I'd provided no evidence that they could ever work. A few people flapping about with wings strapped to them was only going to make it look like we'd worked so hard on the statue that we'd lost our minds.

Undaunted, I went straight into the 'Malik Rolling Platform Bridge'. He said this was better, because it was an attempt to solve a genuine problem. Engineers do need to create bridges that boats can pass underneath, so this is a good starting point.

But he thought my particular solution wasn't very practical. Only a few people could go over at once, so it wouldn't function as well as a traditional bridge. And it wouldn't work for locomotives, or even carriages, as the horses might take fright halfway across and leap into the river.

I had only one idea left now, so I had to put everything into it. I reminded him of his love for the Thames Tunnel, and he agreed that it was a true wonder of engineering. Then I described a rich gentleman and lady riding all the way to the edge of our beautiful nation in their carriage, feeling sad that they had to turn back, but then discovering the Malik Tunnel and continuing on to England.

Instead of pointing out problems with the idea, Monsieur Eiffel grabbed his notebook and started to sketch diagrams and jot down numbers. It was obvious this one had excited him, and I was half expecting him to announce it would be our next project before Leila had even presented her idea.

But he snapped out of his trance and told her to go ahead.

She held up her tower diagram, which was basically just a tall triangle. She gave a speech about how amazing it would be to climb into the sky and look down upon our great city. You could spend hours watching people sauntering around parks, rushing along streets and lounging about in cafes. The tower would become a famous landmark, and a lasting monument to the power of engineering.

Monsieur Eiffel turned to a new page in his book and scribbled again. After a few minutes of confusing silence, I asked him which of us had won.

He folded his arms and said we'd both done very well, but unfortunately, he wouldn't pick either idea as his next project.

He said that my tunnel idea was a brilliant solution that would meet a genuine need. A tunnel under the sea would bring two great countries closer. It would be a spectacular feat of engineering, and he was sure that it would be possible.

But it would be a huge, expensive undertaking that would require delicate diplomatic work before the first lump of soil was taken from the ground. The French and British governments would both have to approve the idea, and agree how to fund it, something that would take years rather than months.

Then he turned to my sister and said her tower would be a true marvel of engineering, but it didn't really solve a problem. People want to go further and faster, but we have no evidence they want to go upwards too. It would cost millions of francs, and as it didn't particularly benefit any company or branch of government, he couldn't imagine who would fund it.

My sister said we should take out a loan, and charge people to climb the tower when it is finished. Monsieur Eiffel had to calmly explain why this wasn't realistic.

He said it didn't really matter anyway, because the good news was that he'd been offered a new contract already. He's just been asked to design a large iron hall for the headquarters of the bank Crédit Lyonnais. They'll be able to pay much better than Monsieur Bartholdi did, and they'll let him take longer too, which will give us a chance to learn mechanical drawing on a real project.

I told him it sounded great, but the truth is that I was a little disappointed we weren't doing my tunnel idea.

Leila: Even if I were to admit that your tunnel idea is actually very good, Malik, you can't deny how difficult it would be to set up. You can't just burrow into someone's country and shout 'surprise!'

My tower, on the other hand, could

really happen. My idea of charging people a few francs to climb it would work. Everyone in the whole city would want to go up, and so would any tourist who ever came here. You'd cover building costs and be into profit in no time.

August 5th

Malik: The Crédit Lyonnais building covers a whole block on the Boulevard des Italiens in the second arrondissement. We're going to design an iron hall with two rows of balconies to add to the back. It will be a bright, open space that will be pleasant for the workers, and help managers to spot if someone isn't working hard enough.

And talking of people who don't work hard enough, Leila did nothing but sulk today. Monsieur Eiffel handed us both rough drawings of the iron parts we're going to make for the hall. I sat on the front desk with him, and he showed me how to use my rulers and pencils to present a solid object on flat paper.

Leila took her rough drawing to the table at the back of the studio, but made no attempt to turn it into a neat diagram. She just muttered to herself and drew long, scruffy triangles. I'm not sure what those had to do with the hall.

`Leila: The triangles were pictures of my tower, obviously. I still think it's a great idea. If Monsieur Eiffel doesn't want to build it, I will. I know it can work. I just need someone to lend me the money.`

August 6th

Malik: Monsieur Eiffel wanted us to take some of the finished diagrams over to Monsieur Germain, the owner of Crédit Lyonnais. I was enjoying my drawing, and wasn't keen on running out on an errand. But to my surprise, my sister offered to take them.

She moaned so much about carrying the iron straps to Monsieur Bartholdi that I was amazed she wanted to do this. She's probably just realised she'll never be as good at mechanical drawing as me, so she's looking for something else to do.

Leila: I grabbed the diagrams and headed over to the Boulevard des Italiens. The front part of the Crédit Lyonnais building is already built and is in use. It has a grand stone front with pillars around an arched entrance. Inside, there is a wide staircase spiralling around to the first floor.

A guard in a black hat asked me what I wanted, and I told him I had important

documents to deliver to Monsieur Germain. He said I should leave them with him, but I insisted on taking them personally.

He led me up the staircase and to a wooden door. I knocked, went in and saw a small man sitting behind a wide desk. He was bald, with a greying beard and moustache, deep-set eyes and the pale complexion of someone who spends their life in an office. He had a huge pile of papers and was signing them with his quill.

I told Monsieur Germain who I was, and handed him the plans. He said that they all looked in order, and went back to his work.

I knew I should have gone, but I couldn't stop myself. I'd jumped at the chance to deliver the diagrams for a reason, and it wasn't time to back out now.

I asked Monsieur Germain if it would be possible to take up an extra moment of his time. He glanced at his pocket watch and said okay, but I'd better make it quick.

I'd planned to go through my full presentation about the tower, but

I could tell Monsieur Germain was impatient, so I cut right to the end.

I told him I wanted to build the biggest tower the world had ever seen, and I needed to borrow some money for it. I said it would be a major project, but so many people would pay to climb the tower that it would make the money back in no time. Then I'd

give him his loan back and half of any extra profits.

He asked me how much money I was hoping to borrow. It was at this point that I realised I hadn't really done any calculations yet. I could remember Monsieur Eiffel saying it would cost millions of francs, but he didn't say how many exactly.

I decided to go on the low side, and work out the details after I'd hooked Monsieur Germain in. I said it would cost one and a half million francs.

Monsieur Germain burst out laughing and said I'd brightened up his day. None of his staff would ever have had the nerve to ask for a loan of one and a half million francs for such a crazy idea. Of course I couldn't have the money, but Monsieur Eiffel should be congratulated for training such fearless staff.

I thanked him for his time and left.

I suppose one and a half million francs was quite a lot to ask for. I thought I could make him forget about the money by inspiring him, but he is a banker after all. They don't get to sit in fancy offices like that by throwing money at everything that excites them.

GET REAL

The Crédit Lyonnaise headquarters were built in the 'Haussmannian' style. This means it was influenced by Georges-Eugène Haussmann, who rebuilt much of Paris in the middle of the 19th century. He tore down cramped slums and replaced them with wide boulevards lined with stone buildings.

As well as looking grander, these new streets may have also been useful for the government. It was much harder to build barricades across these new roads, making it easier for the army to crush uprisings.

August 7th

Malik: When I got to the studio this morning, I had no choice but to tell Monsieur Eiffel what my sister had done. She was meant to have been delivering important papers to one of our customers, but tried to push her own idea instead without permission.

Fortunately, Monsieur Germain was able to see the funny side, and no harm was caused. But with a less forgiving client, the whole project could have been put at risk. Monsieur Eiffel was very angry and told Leila she wouldn't be allowed to carry out any errands like that again. My sister rushed towards me, screwed up the drawing I was working on and stomped out. I suggested to Monsieur Eiffel that he focus on training me alone from now on.

Leila: Alright, Malik. Maybe I shouldn't have ruined your drawing. But there was no need for you to tell Monsieur Eiffel about what happened. You only told him to make me look bad and yourself look better.

But I'm not going to apologise for trying to get my brilliant tower made. If Monsieur Eiffel thinks a hall for a bank is a suitable follow-up to the Liberty Statue, then perhaps he's not the genius everyone makes him out to be.

August 8th

Malik: My sister wasn't in the office today, and wouldn't admit what she'd been up to. Perhaps she'd like me to tell father about her absence. I'm sure there are plenty of things she could be helping out with around the home if she doesn't care about the opportunities Monsieur Eiffel is giving us.

Leila: I couldn't face another day of trying to work when all I could think about was the tower, so I decided to walk around the city instead.

I found myself wandering down to the Seine and crossing over the Île de la Cité to the left bank. It was lined with booksellers standing next to their bright green boxes. Smart gentlemen were browsing dusty volumes and haggling over prices.

I wondered if I should pick a book at random and find a different interest. Engineering didn't seem to be working out too well, after all.

But who else would give a girl a chance to learn anything other than housework? No one would show me the kindness Monsieur Eiffel had done. Perhaps it was time to get back to the studio and immerse myself in the bank project.

I was about to turn back when I spotted something that changed my mind. Maybe my dream wasn't over after all.

August 9th

Malik: I took the diary back from my sister this morning and read her last entry. I know she wants me to ask her what she saw, but I'm not going to.

Leila: The thing that changed my mind, if you must know, was a notice announcing a major exhibition next year. It will be called the 'Exposition Universelle', and will mark 100 years since the revolution. It will showcase the best of modern art, science and technology, with special performances and exhibitions. It will take place throughout the city, but the main site will be the Champ de Mars, on the left bank of the Seine.

It was the last paragraph that really got my heart racing. It said dazzling new buildings would be constructed especially for the event, including the 'Gallery of Machines', which was to be a giant pavilion made of iron and glass.

I stood frozen, staring at the poster. If the committee in charge of the exhibition were prepared to build a huge pavilion, surely they'd want a tower too?

The more I thought about it, the more I realised how perfect it would be. Engineering is the great art of our age, so of course it should be the centrepiece of such a celebration.

At the bottom of the notice, it said the man in charge of the exhibition was Édouard Lockroy, the Minister of Commerce and Industry.

I walked over to the Champ de Mars to examine the site. There was a strip of parkland right next to the river that would be perfect for the tower. I paced around it, counting my steps so I could estimate the total area.

Back in the studio today, I worked up my idea in full, using the size of the park to determine the dimensions of the tower.

I know Monsieur Eiffel will only repeat his objections if I tell him about my plan, which is why I'm heading to the Palais Bourbon on my own tomorrow to find Monsieur Lockroy.

GET REAL

On 14th July 1789, a group of rioters stormed the Bastille, a royal fortress and prison. This event is regarded as the start of the French Revolution, a period of turmoil that saw the execution of King Louis XVI and his wife Marie Antoinette. A huge exhibition was held in 1889 to mark the 100-year anniversary of it.

August 10th

Malik: I see my sister is still obsessed with her tower. By the time she realises it could never happen, I'll be so much better than her at mechanical drawing that she'll never catch up.

Leila: I crossed the river this morning and gazed up at the stone front of the Palais Bourbon, with its wide relief and rows of tall columns. I knew this was where the politicians were, but I had no idea how to get in to them.

The main entrance was a wide arch on the south side, flanked by statues. Two guards were standing beside it, politely greeting the men who were hurrying inside.

I had my diagrams clasped in my hands, and was hoping they might let me deliver them to Monsieur Lockroy if I pretended that he was expecting them. It had worked at the bank, but it turned out that the Palais worked on different rules.

The guards said I wouldn't be allowed inside under any circumstances, and ordered me to leave. I took a few steps back, and kept my eye on the men streaming in and out of the doorway. Maybe they could help.

A man with a bushy black beard sped out, so I jogged alongside him and asked if Monsieur Lockroy was inside the building. He said he had no time for that radical's dangerous ideas, and wasn't prepared to discuss him. I took that as a 'yes'.

A man with a chinstrap beard was striding towards the entrance, so I spun around and followed him. I asked if he could tell Monsieur Lockroy that someone was waiting outside for him. He said that Monsieur Lockroy had abandoned all his principles, and he had no intention of ever speaking to him again.

Next I followed a man with bushy grey side whiskers, who also disliked Monsieur Lockroy, but was at least prepared to give me a description of him. He said he had a long moustache that was slightly curled at the corners, grey hair parted on the left, small frog-like eyes, and the haunted expression of someone who knows they've forgotten their values.

I don't think Monsieur Lockroy would have been happy with the description, but I was. After two hours of waiting, I saw someone who fitted it rushing out, and I chased after him.

He admitted he was Monsieur Lockroy, and I launched into my presentation about the tower. I was hoping he'd stop and look at my plans, but he kept scurrying along, and I had to run after him and shout as he went east along the Seine.

Walking and talking made me mix everything up, and Monsieur Lockroy said he had no idea what I was talking about, and that if I couldn't express it in a single sentence, there was no point going on.

I said I wanted to build a huge tower on the Champ de Mars that would be the centrepiece of next year's exhibition. He said his committee had already looked at the possibility of a stone tower, but it had been too expensive, and there had been many safety fears.

I had the minister's attention. This was my big chance to sell the idea to him and make it happen.

I told him that this wasn't going to be a stone tower. It would be made from iron, the great material of our age. Using iron would make it cheaper, and mean we could safely build to a height that would astonish the world.

I cried that this would be the first ever 300-metre tower.

Monsieur Lockroy came to a stop, and I thrust my plans into his hands. He looked over them, muttering to himself. Then, as if breaking from a spell, he asked who I was and what made me think I could build the biggest structure in the world.

I said I was the finest young engineer in the land, and the Leila Tower would be my breakthrough work.

He scowled and said he must have been crazy to stop and listen to a child on such a busy day. He said the finest architects and artists needed his attention, and he had no idea why he was wasting it on someone who looked like they should be building a tower made from toy bricks rather than iron.

He was turning away again when I told him that I'd given him the wrong name for the tower. It was actually called 'The Eiffel Tower', because it was the idea of the world's greatest engineer, Gustave Eiffel.
Now Monsieur Lockroy was interested

again. He flicked back through my diagrams, and even glanced over my shoulder in the direction of the Champ de Mars, no doubt imagining how the tower would look.

He told me he'd come and see Monsieur Eiffel at 10AM on the 14th, but he would need detailed costings by then. I agreed, and he darted away.

I stood where he had left me for a while, feeling stunned. My tower idea could actually happen. But I'd exaggerated Monsieur Eiffel's involvement slightly. I'd have to get him on board as soon as I could.

Malik: Slight exaggeration? It was a total lie. I shall tell Monsieur Eiffel about your dishonesty when I get to the office tomorrow, and I wouldn't be surprised if he asked you to stay at home from now on.

August 11th

Malik: We both started to speak at once as soon as we arrived at the studio. Monsieur Eiffel looked up from his work, but could only hear the babbling of our competing voices. He held up his hands to silence us, and told us to talk one at a time. He chose my sister to go first, and as it turned out, I never got to give my side of the story.

Leila: It wasn't meant to be a speech. It's just that I'd thought so much about what I wanted to say that it all tumbled out. I told Monsieur Eiffel about the exhibition, and how I'd thought the tower would be perfect for it. I confessed to how I'd met the minister in charge of it and that now he wanted to meet Monsieur Eiffel.

I told Monsieur Eiffel that the leading men of every field would be taking part, so it was only natural that he should represent engineering. He nodded to himself, and I knew I was winning him over.

I think Malik was expecting Monsieur Eiffel to be angry with me for lying, but he got so excited about the exhibition that he didn't mention it.

Monsieur Eiffel told me to sit next to him on the front table, in the seat where Malik usually works. He said we needed to work out if a 300-metre iron tower was mathematically possible, and how much it would cost.

Malik pulled another chair over, sat next to us and asked if there was anything he could do, but Monsieur Eiffel was too lost in his calculations.

By the end of the day, Monsieur Eiffel was talking as if he really had come up with the project and had been backing it all along.

Malik has also mysteriously started to think the tower is a good idea now Monsieur Eiffel likes it, even though he stated in these very pages yesterday that it would never happen.

Chapter 5

Making plans

August 12th

Malik: We spent today refining the plans for our tower. Whilst my sister's diagram was nothing more than a thin triangle with some clouds at the top, Monsieur Eiffel has come up with a practical design that will actually work.

The new tower has a square base with four legs of criss-crossing iron that Monsieur Eiffel calls 'lattice girders'. The legs slope towards each other and eventually join together, creating a slightly curved shape rather than the crude triangle my sister had imagined.

It looks very pleasing, but Monsieur Eiffel says he wasn't trying to make it beautiful. He just calculated the shape that would be best at resisting high winds. But he was glad I liked it. If others did, we might be able to sell a few souvenir models, and put the money towards building costs.

The tower shall have three platforms. There will be a wide one near the bottom supported by an arch, a narrower one at the point the legs begin to meet, and a small one at the top. Above the top one, he'll build a laboratory for studying the weather and observing the stars.

Deep concrete foundations will be laid beneath each leg. The weight of the whole thing will be over 7,000 tons, which sounds like a lot, but is actually very light. You could melt the whole thing down and it would cover the square base in the Champ de Mars with a thickness of just a few centimetres.

Every time Monsieur Eiffel made a rough sketch, I turned it into a neat diagram, and he said my technical drawing skills were coming along well. Leila tried to do a diagram too, but I noticed she'd added several doodles to the side, so she clearly wasn't concentrating.

Leila: I wasn't doodling. I was actually coming up with a dramatic way to show how high the tower is. I drew it on one side of the diagram, and on the other I drew Notre-Dame, the Statue of Liberty, the Arc de Triomphe, and the column from Place Vendôme all piled on top of one another, and still not matching the tower's height.

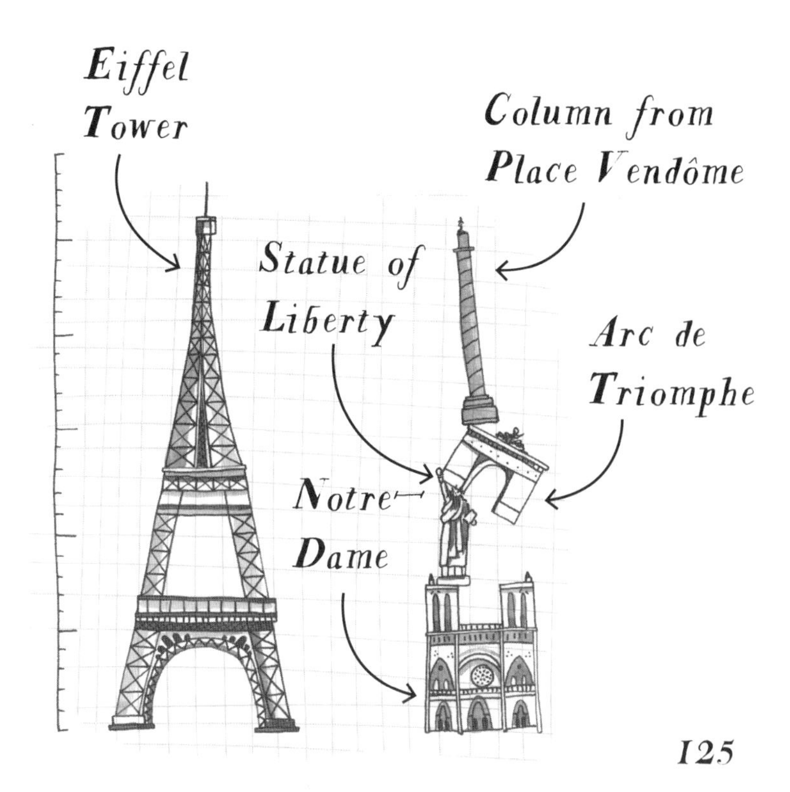

I gave it to Monsieur Eiffel, and he promised to make it part of his presentation. There's no way Monsieur Lockroy can reject the idea now. Monsieur Eiffel has proved that my dream of a 300-metre tower can be realised after all.

August 13th

Malik: Monsieur Eiffel spent today working out how much the tower would cost, which meant a lot of jotting down numbers. I asked if he needed any help, but he said it would be much better if we just sat in silence and didn't interrupt his calculations.

After two hours of muttering to himself, Monsieur Eiffel announced that the tower would cost 6,500,000 francs.

Leila: I think that's pretty expensive, isn't it? I don't really know, because I've never had to buy a 300-metre tower before. They don't exactly sell them at the markets.

But Monsieur Eiffel is convinced that the government will easily make their money back through entry tickets and souvenir replicas, so I'm sure it will be fine.

August 14th

Malik: We rearranged the studio this morning so we could present our ideas to Monsieur Lockroy properly. We moved the tables to the sides of the room and then carried wooden boxes up from the courtyard to make a small stage. We then arranged a line of chairs in front of them.

Monsieur Lockroy arrived on time, and brought another man with him, who had a white beard, black eyebrows and a sullen expression. He introduced himself as Jean-Charles Adolphe Alphand. Monsieur Eiffel seemed to know him. It turned out the man was also an engineer. Monsieur Lockroy had brought him along to check our design was actually possible.

Monsieur Eiffel began his presentation, and we applauded and commented on how brilliant it was at every opportunity.

At one point, Monsieur Alphand asked to see the diagrams, and there were a few tense moments as he leafed through them. When he announced that the calculations were sound, we both jumped and cheered, making our wooden boxes wobble.

Monsieur Eiffel continued the presentation, but shifted to his plans for a scientific laboratory at the top, which could be used long after the exhibition was over.

Monsieur Lockroy was so excited he didn't even wait for the presentation to end properly before proclaiming that the tower would be ideal for the exhibition. Monsieur Alphand agreed, and we cheered again.

Monsieur Eiffel then ran them through the prices of materials and labour before announcing that the cost of the tower would be 6,500,000 francs. He thanked both gentlemen for coming to see him and said he was looking forward to working with them.

The two men stared down at their feet in silence. Monsieur Eiffel asked them if something was wrong.

After an uncomfortable pause, Monsieur Lockroy admitted they only had 1,500,000 francs left in their budget. They'd already committed to building the Gallery of the Machines, the Palace of the Fine Arts and the Palace of the Liberal Arts, and could offer nothing more.

Monsieur Eiffel explained how they could make the money back through tourism, but the men said further funds wouldn't be possible.

At this point, my sister leapt down from her box and pretty much begged them to build the tower. She asked if they could combine the liberal arts and the fine arts into one palace to save money, but the men said that work on them had already begun.

They said Monsieur Eiffel should consider designing a smaller tower that could be built on their budget. If he couldn't, they'd look back at some of the other proposals they'd received, such as the giant commemorative guillotine.

Leila: I couldn't believe it. My tower dream had collapsed, and it was all because of money. Monsieur Lockroy and Monsieur Alphand loved everything about it, but they just couldn't afford to build it.

It didn't seem right. All the time Monsieur Eiffel was presenting, and we were cheering him on, it seemed like it was fated to happen.

Even now, I can't imagine walking past the Champs de Mars next year without the tower being there.

GET REAL

One of the exhibits proposed for the 1889 Exposition Universelle was a giant statue of a guillotine, a machine for beheading people that became a symbol of the French Revolution. Thousands were executed on the guillotine during the 'reign of terror' that followed the revolution. Perhaps Paris would be seen as a less romantic city if a huge killing machine loomed over it, rather than a tower?

August 15th

Malik: We returned to our work on the bank today. My sister went back to sulking in the corner, whilst I continued working on my technical drawings.

Monsieur Eiffel didn't say much to me, even though I thought my diagrams were very good. He kept glancing over at his tower plans, and I think he's almost as upset as Leila that it isn't going ahead. But what can we do? It's not happening, so let's focus on the work we've been commissioned to do.

A banking hall might not be as exciting as a giant tower, but we can make it the best one in the world if we all try our best.

`Leila: I still can't believe the tower isn't going to be built. When I look over the tops of Paris' buildings, I can see a huge gap in the sky where it's meant to go.`

August 16th

Malik: Monsieur Eiffel didn't arrive in the studio until the middle of the morning.

He strolled in, humming to himself and immediately began rolling up the diagrams of the banking hall. This is something he usually does at the end of a project, and for a moment I thought my sister had somehow managed to annoy Monsieur Germain again and he'd cancelled the job.

But when I asked him what was going on, Monsieur Eiffel said he'd passed the bank hall on to another studio because we wouldn't have time to work on it.

Before he could say anything else, my sister leapt up and asked if this was because we were going to build the tower instead.

He said we were, and she clapped her hands and danced around the room.

Monsieur Eiffel said he'd just been to sign the contract with Monsieur Lockroy and Monsieur Alphand. He'd promised to complete the tower in time for the exhibition in May, so there was no time to lose.

I asked him how they'd managed to find the extra money, and he said they hadn't. He'd agreed to fund it himself, as long as he could keep all the profits. My sister was still leaping around and cheering, and wasn't listening. Perhaps she wasn't interested in the small detail that Monsieur Eiffel has just committed to spending 6,500,000 francs, and was gambling all of his fortune on the tower being a success.

This really has to be the greatest tower ever, because if no one goes to see it, Monsieur Eiffel will be bankrupt, and we'll be out of work too.

Leila: Lighten up, Malik. Stop worrying for once in your life and celebrate. The tower is going to be built, it will be the most astonishing thing ever, and we'll be part of it.

GET REAL

The committee in charge of the Exposition Universelle, which included Édouard Lockroy and Jean-Charles Adolphe Alphand, agreed that Gustave Eiffel's tower should be the centrepiece of their exhibition. But they could only pay 1,500,000 francs towards the 6,500,000 cost. Eiffel made up the difference with his own money, and was entitled to the profit generated by entrance fees, souvenir models and the cafes inside the tower for the next twenty years.

August 24th

Malik: Our work has begun. The tower will require 18,000 parts, and Eiffel needs to make precise calculations for all of them.

I asked if I could turn his notes into full diagrams, but he said he wouldn't have time to look over my work. Everything would have to be done by Monsieur Koechlin's drawing office. Instead, he wanted us to keep the project running whilst he was working.

We'd take his notes to the drawing office, take the finished diagrams to the foundry and visit the Champ de Mars to check on progress.

I thought Leila might consider these tasks were beneath her, but for once, she's not complaining.

Leila: Of course I'm not. Every little thing I can do to make the tower a reality suits me fine. Everyone in the offices and foundry is excited. Even Armand isn't complaining when he gets new parts to make, which must be his equivalent of jumping for joy.

Chapter 6

Shaky foundations

September 25th

Malik: Work has started on the four foundations in the Champ de Mars. Although it feels like we aren't really building the tower yet, this is the most important part of all. Monsieur Eiffel says that even the slightest mistake in the foundations could affect the whole thing, and maybe make it unstable.

I accompanied Monsieur Eiffel around the four sites as the workers dug deep into the ground. He jumped into the pits as they were being excavated to check the soil. He's concerned about the legs nearest to the river, where the dig has hit soft clay, but he's sure they'll hit thicker, drier clay as they go further down.

Each foundation will consist of 6 metres of cement and limestone boulders with huge anchoring bolts set into the middle. Monsieur

Eiffel will fit powerful pistons into the bolts that will allow him to make tiny adjustments to the legs so they can align perfectly when it's time to fix the first stage on.

Monsieur Eiffel was just telling me how pleased he was with our progress when he had to go and sort out some problem caused by Leila. A complete waste of his precious time.

Leila: I can't help it if some stupid onlookers misunderstood me. Whilst Malik followed Monsieur Eiffel around and annoyed him, I set myself the more important task of getting rid of the crowds that were starting to form around the digs.

It seemed that everyone who was passing along the Seine chose to come and stare at us. I went around calmly asking them to leave and explaining that there was nothing to see yet.

Most people agreed, but by the time I'd cleared one crowd, another would emerge at a different pit.

It got exhausting, and when I spotted some giggling boys throwing stones into one of the holes, I lost my temper. I told them that messing with the foundations could affect the stability of the whole tower.

My message was passed on through the crowd until it grew into the rumour that the tower would fall over and

crush everyone if a single stray stone fell into one of the pits. Eventually this nonsense reached some of the people in the apartment blocks lining the park.

They marched over to Monsieur Eiffel and demanded to know whether the tower would crush them in their sleep.

Monsieur Eiffel had to calmly take them through his plans, which they'd all seen before anyway, and explain why it wouldn't happen. Even after he'd convinced them that the tower was safe, they still insisted on moaning about how it would spoil their views.

I couldn't believe how ungrateful they were. The greatest structure in the world was about to go up right in front of their houses, and all they could do was complain. I'd love to live right next to it.

When the last of the unfriendly neighbours had gone, Monsieur Eiffel told me not to speak to any members of the public about the tower again. They could follow the announcements in the newspapers if they wanted to learn about it.

November 4th

Malik: The foundations are now complete, and construction is beginning on the legs. The crowds are getting bigger every day, and everyone in the city is talking about the tower.

Not everyone likes it as much as we do, unfortunately. A group of writers, musicians and artists has formed to try and stop it being built, as they believe it will be so ugly it will ruin the city. They have added their names to a letter in the newspaper *Le Temps* that claims the tower will be a disfiguring blot on the beauty of Paris.

They have called the tower a 'half-built factory chimney', an 'ungainly skeleton' and a 'tragic street lamp'. It seems obvious to me that all these people are jealous that their artistic work isn't getting as much attention as the tower. If these attacks are upsetting Monsieur Eiffel, he isn't letting it show. He says these critics know nothing about the scientific uses of the tower, and he can't do much about it if they consider it unattractive.

Leila, on the other hand, is fuming. She spent all day ranting to herself and scrawling out a reply to send to *Le Temps*.

Leila: Of course I'm angry. I love the tower, and anyone attacking it might as well be attacking me.

Here is my letter:

Dear artistic people,

Thank you so much for your thoughts on the tower that we are building for the Exposition Universelle.

I'm sorry if it doesn't please you, but I can assure you that we think it's very beautiful. Perhaps you'll agree when you see its sleek, curved lines rising from the Champ de Mars next year.

But even if you don't, you must agree that a great feat of construction can be as inspiring as any work of art. Do we love the pyramids of Egypt because they're beautiful? Or because we marvel at their creation? Could it be that future peoples will look back on this landmark as a crowning achievement of our own age?

Perhaps your objection is not to the tower, but to engineering itself? You see it as a means to an end, but not as an art in itself. You see its practitioners such as the great Monsieur Eiffel as mere craftsmen, but never artists to be ranked alongside yourselves.

But like the tower, engineering is rising above all else in this era of science, and there is nothing you can do to halt it.

Our tower deserves to be the centrepiece of the exhibition, and of our great city.

Cordialement,

Leila Saadia

Chief Assistant to Gustave Eiffel

GET REAL

A large group of artists protested against the Eiffel Tower when it was announced. They included the author Guy de Maupassant, the artists William-Adolphe Bouguereau and Ernest Meissonier, and the architect Charles Garnier. Many of them changed their minds when the tower was completed, though some kept up their objections for years. It's said that Guy de Maupassant ate his lunch beneath the Eiffel Tower every day, as it was the only place in the city he couldn't see it from.

November 5th

Malik: Monsieur Lockroy replied to the grumpy artists in *Le Temps* today. He said that none of the great places in Paris would change because of the tower, except for the Champ de Mars, which he hadn't noticed any of them painting or writing poems about recently. He said that the tower would become a wonderful symbol of the city, and if they didn't agree, it didn't matter, as work had already begun on it. But he congratulated them on the passionate argument of their letter, and offered to place it in the exhibition.

Leila: Ahem. My letter also appeared in *Le Temps* today. I know you're only refusing to mention it because I listed myself as Monsieur Eiffel's chief assistant.

December 10th

Malik: Every day, the foundry finish more pieces of the tower, and send them by cart to the Champ de Mars. Monsieur Eiffel doesn't want any of the parts to get mixed up, so he's got our workers to join them into sections with temporary bolts. When they reach the site, the bolts are replaced with red-hot rivets. These smaller sections can then be pieced together like a giant jigsaw.

We accompanied some of these sections from the foundry to the Champ de Mars today, to make sure no harm came to them. It's just as well we did, because some young children followed behind the cart and tried to touch the overhanging pieces.

Leila foolishly told them to stop because the metal was going to be part of the new tower in the Champ de Mars. Obviously, this made them even more determined to paw at it, and the cart had to speed up, leaving us running behind and shielding the metal from the many eager children.

Leila: Maybe I shouldn't have admitted what it was. But I still find it hard to keep quiet about the tower, because I'm so excited about it. But it didn't matter in the end. We eventually managed to lose the children and deliver the parts to Monsieur Compagnon, who is overseeing the 250 workmen who are assembling the tower.

December 15th

Malik: We spent today wandering around the site, and checking the legs as they were being constructed.

As I was looking at the north leg, I heard a huge clatter behind me, and spun around to see a pile of long iron poles scattered like firewood. A workman dressed in baggy corduroy trousers, a red cap and a tight grey jacket clambered down and gathered them up.

He apologised and said he'd taken the temporary bolts out and the whole thing had collapsed.

He asked if I knew how to put them back together. I'd spent so long gazing at all the diagrams coming out of the drawing office that I was sure I could. It looked like one of the latticed strips that criss-cross each other inside the legs, and I'd seen plenty of those.

The workman called one of his friends down and I told them where all the pieces went whilst they fitted the bolts back in.

When they were finished, it looked pretty good. Some of the smaller iron strips seemed to be going in weird directions, but I expected it would be fine once it was in place.

They tied a rope around it and were about to lift it back up when my sister came running over. We discussed it and decided it would be better to take the section back on the cart so Monsieur Eiffel could check it had been reassembled properly.

Leila: No, Malik. Not to check it had been reassembled properly, but to take it apart and start again from scratch. It was obvious that the wonky abomination you created was wrong. Hardly any of the strips were in the right places and the whole thing looked about as stable as a plate of macarons.

This isn't the time to show off to workmen by pretending to know things you don't. Every piece of the tower is important. We can't have one of the legs giving way so the whole thing totters over like a three-legged chair, just because you wanted to look like an expert.

January 5th

Malik: The four legs are now 25 metres high, and Monsieur Eiffel has halted work so we can build wooden scaffolding to support them. This was always his plan, but that didn't stop nosey people from asking what was going on. A few rude onlookers even asked if we had abandoned the tower because it was unstable.

I ignored everyone, though I spotted Leila talking to someone.

Leila: I only spoke to one man. He said he was very worried about the tower falling on his house, and I felt sorry for him. I told him the scaffolding was always going to be the next step, and was needed to make sure the legs didn't collapse inwards. I said the workers would be back in a few days, and all would be back to normal soon. He said I'd put his mind at rest, and walked away, scribbling in a notebook.

January 6th

Malik: The front page of *Le Temps* today was a picture of the four abandoned legs with the headline, 'Eiffel assistant admits tower will collapse without scaffolding'. The story went on to suggest the whole project was about to be cancelled on safety grounds.

Here's a tip, Leila. Next time somebody with a notebook comes over to you and asks the sort of questions a journalist would ask, it's just possible that they might not be who they say they are.

`Leila: Oh, who cares what the newspapers write, anyway? They've already dismissed the tower as a stupid idea. It's what the public will think that counts. And I'm convinced they'll love it.`

February 4th

Malik: The legs are complete and have been joined by four long iron trusses. This is a big moment, as it means we can start on the first platform, which will be strong enough to hold cafes, bars and hundreds of visitors.

Monsieur Eiffel spent hours adjusting the pistons until each leg was lined up perfectly. The tower might be 300 metres tall, but he needs everything to be perfect to the last millimetre.

Leila: Let's hope this puts an end to all the silly rumours about the tower collapsing. With the four legs joined together, it's obvious that this wide, sturdy shape isn't going to crash into someone's bedroom anytime soon.

Chapter 7

Coming together

February 20th

Malik: The first stage is complete now, and all the workmen have moved their equipment up to it. There are four cranes, as well as twenty forges for the riveters, and a canteen so the men don't have to waste time going down for lunch.

Leila: It's very strange to walk around the legs and hear the shouting and clanking of hammers above. You can see the smoke from the forges and the movement of the cranes beyond. It's as if there's a totally different city far above you.

February 24th

Malik: The stairs to the first platform are complete, so it's easy to get there. You climb 350 steps, holding onto a railing, and through the criss-crossing iron you can see the ground getting gradually further away.

Once you reach the platform, however, things get trickier. The next stage of the iron framework already reaches high above it, and the workmen climb the latticework as if it were a giant slanting ladder.

Monsieur Eiffel has instructed the men to build small wooden platforms to work on, so none of them get vertigo. The platforms have no railings around them, just a 100-metre drop, yet the men work as casually as if they were on the ground.

Some of them are even insisting they don't need the platforms. I saw a man sitting on a horizontal girder and reading a newspaper during his lunch break. A particularly surprising story could have made him keel over backwards and splat down onto the first stage.

We are still meant to be checking the work against Monsieur Eiffel's plans, but I'm going to do it from the safety of the first stage. I really can't face climbing up to one of those platforms.

Leila: Well I did what I was meant to, at least. I clambered up the west side of the tower until I reached a wooden platform that was secured by ropes to two girders.

The workmen bent down to grab my hand as I approached. They pulled me up and joked about how I'd got there quicker than them. I examined their work and said it was all going to plan.

Then I leaned over the edge of the wobbly platform and looked at the world far below. It seemed much stiller from up there. From the first platform, you can still make out people, carriages and boats moving around. But higher up, they're just distant, slow-moving blobs.

To the south, you can see the framework of the Gallery of the Machines and the Palaces of Fine and Liberal Arts going up. How quickly this unremarkable stretch of sandy park is becoming the most exciting place in the world.

February 26th

Malik: I was carrying out my inspections from the first platform when one of the workers shouted down and asked if I could bring his hammer up. His wooden ledge was only about 15 metres above the platform, and I felt like I should try my best, especially given that Leila has been scampering up and down the framework with no problem.

I grabbed the hammer from the toolbox next to my feet, stuffed it into the back of my belt and went up. The workers make climbing the diagonal bars look easy, but I found that my feet kept slipping to the side and I had to grip the bars above me to keep from falling off.

I pulled myself up slowly, trying to focus on my climbing rather than worrying about how high I was. My knees felt weak and my hands trembled as I threw them upwards and grasped for new rungs.

I stopped and looked up, hoping I was almost there. I'd barely covered half the distance.

I told myself to keep going, but my right foot slipped slightly and I couldn't stop myself looking down.

It would have been fine if I'd seen just the first platform. But I glanced slightly to the side and saw the ground of the park far below.

My heart pounded and I let out a high whimper. I stayed frozen for a few seconds, and the wind chose that moment to pick up. I was convinced I was about to be blown off and dashed into one of the apartments at the side of the park.

Steadying myself, I took a few deep breaths, and carried on up. The wooden platform was soon looming above me, and a hand grabbed my sleeve and pulled me up. I was glad father had insisted on buying me a good quality jacket. Poor stitching could have sent me to my death.

Woah!

I stood on the wobbly platform and stuck my hands on my hips. My pulse was still racing, but I'd done it. I'd got there.

The workman scowled and pointed down to the platform below. His hammer had fallen out of my belt and landed a few centimetres away from where I'd picked it up.

Leila: Just send me up next time, Malik. I don't have a problem with heights, which is pretty handy seeing as though I'm going to be an engineer. Imagine trying to become one when you can't even climb up a few metres without fainting.

March 8th

Malik: The second stage has now been added and the tower rises above the park like a giant letter 'A'. Next comes the tricky part where the four legs converge. To get the remaining iron sections so high up, Monsieur Eiffel will send mobile cranes up the spaces where the lifts will eventually go.

Fitting everything together in such a restricted space will be a big challenge. And this final section will be taller than the other two combined. But Monsieur Eiffel has it all precisely planned, and if anyone can do it, he can.

Leila: We were walking back home from the tower this evening, and everyone we passed was staring up at it. Two gentlemen even bumped into each other because their eyes were fixed on the strange shape of the tower.

I wanted to stop them and tell them it was my idea, and would be twice as tall when it was finished, but I know I'm forbidden from discussing it with the public, so I kept quiet.

March 14th

Malik: Monsieur Eiffel gathered us on the first platform this afternoon for a special announcement. We have passed 170 metres, so the tower is now the tallest man-made structure in the world. To celebrate, he opened bottles of brandy for the workmen, and gave them the rest of the day off, which was just as well, because you wouldn't want to have sent them up to those tiny platforms afterwards.

Leila: The men suggested a toast to Monsieur Eiffel, but he said he wanted to propose an alternative one. I felt myself blushing, sure that he was going to announce that I'd actually come up with the idea. But instead, he said they should drink a toast to iron, as it was this magnificent material that had ultimately made the tower possible.

To iron! Is there anything it can't do?

GET REAL

The Washington Monument, which is 169 metres high, was the tallest human-made structure in the world when it was completed in 1884. But it only kept the record until the 300-metre Eiffel Tower was built in 1889. The Eiffel Tower held onto the record until the Chrysler Building in New York, which is 319 metres high, was opened in 1930.

The tallest building in the world now is the Burj Khalifa in Dubai, United Arab Emirates, which is 830 metres tall.

March 30th

Malik: It's time to celebrate. After months of exhausting planning and construction, the tower is complete. The lifts still need to be installed, and the cafes and restaurants on the first floor are still being built, but the structure is finished, and it is now possible to climb all the way to the top.

Tomorrow Monsieur Eiffel will lead a party of officials there, but he took Leila and I up today, for a special preview.

To get to the third stage from the second, you need to go up a very narrow spiral staircase with just a thin handrail running around it. Monsieur Eiffel went first, followed by my sister. They were practically running whilst I trod carefully behind them, keeping my eyes on the iron steps. Fortunately, Monsieur Eiffel kept stopping to point out features of his design, so it wasn't hard to catch up.

It took us over an hour to get to the top, so I can see why elevators will be needed for the big crowds. They don't want to find their pleasant afternoon at the exhibition unexpectedly turning into an epic mountain trek.

I arrived at the third stage gasping for breath, with my legs aching. It's much smaller than the other levels, and is just an octagonal platform that lets you view the distant city below. Leila was leaning over the rail and pointing out landmarks, but after a couple of glances down that made me feel weak, I decided to inspect the clouds instead.

A spiral staircase takes you even higher, to the small space where the laboratory will be. Monsieur Eiffel announced that we were the first people ever to have climbed the world's tallest structure, and I felt a swell of pride mixed in with the dizziness and nausea.

Leila: The view from the first and second stages had been dramatic, but the top was something else again. The hill of Montmartre, where Eiffel had taken us to learn about the wind, was a tiny bump to my right. The Seine was a muddy trickle beneath me. And the streets were criss-crossing grey lines, broken by the green strips of the city's parks.

I told Monsieur Eiffel that I couldn't believe this magnificent experience had started with my small diagram. This was partly because the view was genuinely astonishing, and partly to remind him that the original idea for the tower was mine. I don't mind it being known as the Eiffel Tower. It's not as if I could ever have worked out how to make it a reality myself, let alone have paid for it. But some acknowledgement would be nice.

31st March

Malik: Following our preview yesterday, today was the official celebration of the tower's completion. A group of politicians, including Monsieur Lockroy and Monsieur Alphand, and dozens of press reporters, gathered at the base of the tower just after noon.

Monsieur Eiffel welcomed them, and showed them up to the first stage. There were excited cries from the group as they saw their city in a totally new way. After a few minutes, we continued up to the second stage. Some of the older politicians were already out of breath and said they'd wait there for the others.

Eiffel led the rest all the way to the top, and Leila and I followed. A few of the party seemed even less confident than me as we continued the long climb to the third level. I noticed one was trembling as he gripped the hand rail, whilst another grasped the shoulder of the man in front of him.

The group, who had been so talkative on the first stage, were almost completely silent when we got to the third. Perhaps they were listening intently to Monsieur Eiffel's speech so they could report what he'd said. Or perhaps they were just too overwhelmed to speak.

When he had finished telling everyone about all the scientific experiments he was planning from the laboratory, he said it was time to declare the tower officially finished. He yanked on a rope, and a huge tricolour flag unfurled above us.

The men applauded and shouted 'Vive Eiffel!' and 'Vive la France!'

After that, we made our way down to the first platform, where drinks were served to the guests, and Monsieur Eiffel gave a final speech.

Leila: And what did he say in the final speech, Malik? Anything worth mentioning?

Monsieur Eiffel thanked Monsieur Lockroy, Monsieur Alphand and everyone in the government. He also thanked the press, despite all the things they'd written at the start of the project. A few of them looked awkwardly down at their shoes.

Then he said he had one last very special mention to make. I thought he was going to talk about iron again, and I told myself not to get my hopes up. But he actually pointed at me and said I should be thanked for having the original idea for the tower, and believing in it when even he thought it was impossible.

Everyone turned to me and I felt myself flushing deep red. At the end of his speech, the crowd shouted their congratulations again, and Monsieur Eiffel suggested an addition.

Soon everyone, except Malik, joined in a chant of:

Vive La France!
Vive Eiffel!
Vive Leila!

26th May

Malik: The tower has been open to the public for almost two weeks now. We've already had 30,000 visitors, and the lifts have only just gone into action, so numbers will no doubt go up even more.

The prices are two francs to go to the first platform, three francs to go to the second, and five to go all the way to the top, and people have been more than willing to pay. Monsieur Eiffel believes we will get over two million visitors during the exhibition and that he will make his money back very soon.

The buildings on the first and second platforms are all open too. There's a restaurant and bar on the first stage, as well as many souvenir stalls. There's a patisserie on the second platform, and even a newspaper office and printing press, where special daily editions about the exhibition are being produced.

Monsieur Eiffel has also had a desk and some chairs, as well as papers and measuring instruments, brought up to the laboratory above the third platform. Only special guests like us are allowed in there, and I love seeing the faces of the visitors when the guard recognises us and ushers us up the spiral staircase. They may have climbed to the third platform, but some of us can go even higher.

We took father and mother up the tower last week, and meant to show them the laboratory, but they both felt dizzy on the way to the second level and couldn't go any further.

They were very impressed when I said I'd managed to climb up to one of the wooden platforms before the stairs were even built, until Leila interrupted to say that she'd gone even higher.

When we were all back down again, they said how proud they were of us for being part of such an amazing project.

Father even said it had made all their sacrifices worth it, and I noticed mother wiping a tear from her eye.

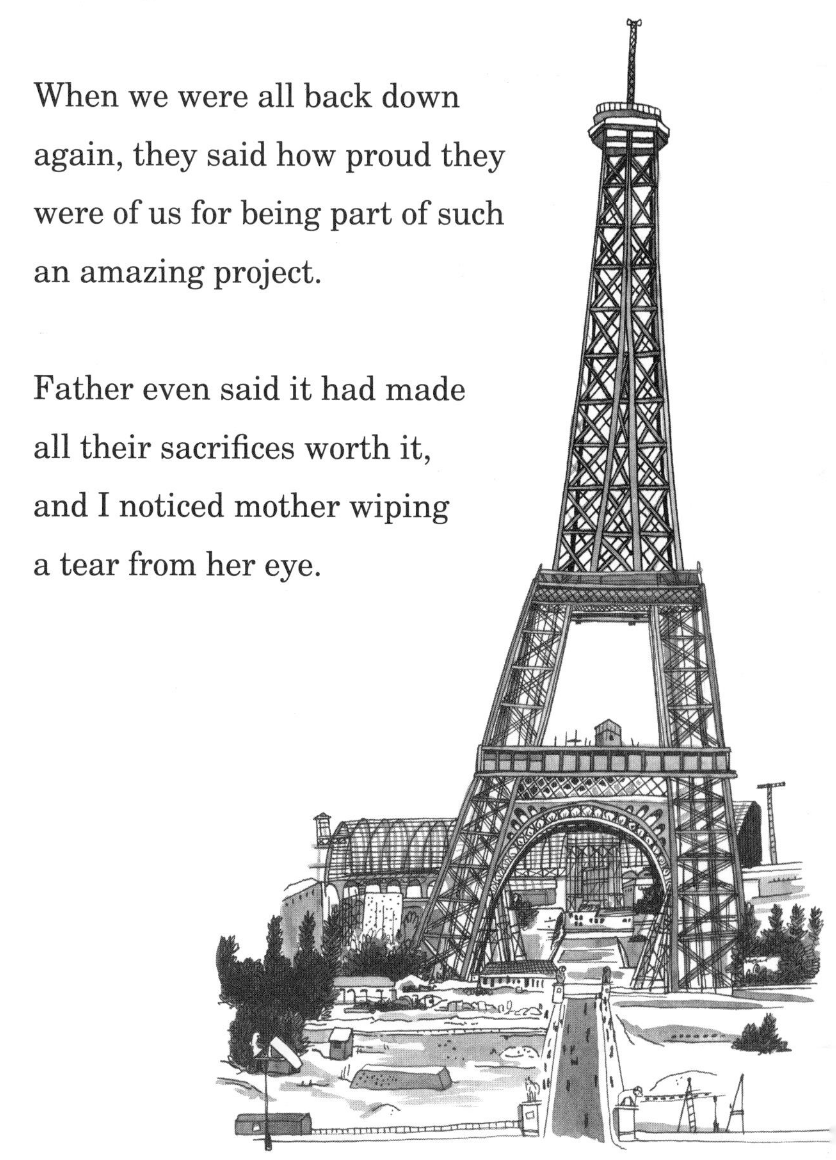

We've spent the last few days in the laboratory, deciding what Monsieur Eiffel's next project should be. I think it's my turn now, and that we should do the tunnel.

Leila: How exactly are you going to explain that to the British politicians? Tell them that your sister got her tower made, so they need to agree to your tunnel just to make it fair?

I hope it does get made, though. We've gone as high as we can into the sky, so under the ground seems like the natural place to go next.

And thanks for starting this diary, and letting me write in it too. It turned out that we had not one, but two extraordinary things to document.

First, the greatest statue ever built, a symbol of liberty that rises high into the sky. And then, the greatest tower ever built, a symbol of science and progress that rises even higher.

Watching both of these go up has been the most amazing experience of my life, and I'm glad we managed to record it as it happened.

Vive La France!

Vive Eiffel!

Vive me!

And just so you don't feel left out…

Vive Malik!

The End

The Statue of Liberty and the Eiffel Tower

Two of the most famous structures in the world were created in Paris in the late 19th century, and they were linked by the great engineer Gustave Eiffel.

The Statue of Liberty, officially known as 'Liberty Enlightening the World', was conceived by the politician Édouard de Laboulaye and the sculptor Frédéric Auguste Bartholdi in 1871. They hoped to give the 46-metre statue as a gift to the United States of America in 1876, which was the 100-year anniversary of the Declaration of Independence. However, funding and building the statue took a little longer than planned.

Bartholdi chose to make the statue from thin sheets of copper. Each sheet was shaped by creating plaster sections, fitting wooden moulds around them and then beating the copper into the moulds.

Gustave Eiffel was commissioned to design an iron framework to support the sheets. The entire statue was constructed in Paris before being dismantled and shipped across the Atlantic.

The statue was built again on its base on Bedloe's Island in New York Harbour, which has since been renamed Liberty Island. It was completed in 1886, and soon became one of the world's most famous landmarks.

Back in Paris, an even taller structure was on the way. Two engineers who worked for Gustave Eiffel, Émile Nouguier and Maurice Koechlin, suggested that a huge iron tower should be created for the upcoming 'Exposition Universelle'.

The design was approved by the French government in 1886, and construction began in early 1887. The structure was completed by March 1889, and opened to the public in May of that year.

Despite some initial criticism of the design, the Eiffel Tower was a huge success, and became a symbol of France in much the same way that the Statue of Liberty came to stand for the whole United States.

Although it was originally only meant to last twenty years, the Eiffel Tower still stands today, and remains one of the most popular tourist attractions in the world.

Timeline

1776

The Thirteen British colonies in North America declare independence from Great Britain and form the United States of America. The Statue of Liberty was originally planned to celebrate the 100-year anniversary of this event.

1789

An armed mob of Parisians storm the Bastille in Paris, an event that is seen as the beginning of the French Revolution. The Eiffel Tower was built to celebrate the 100-year anniversary.

1832

Gustave Eiffel is born in Dijon, France.

Timeline

1871

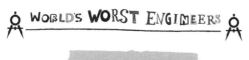

Édouard de Laboulaye and Frédéric Auguste Bartholdi come up with the idea of building a giant statue of Lady Liberty to give to the United States as a gift.

1876

Laboulaye and Bartholdi fail to get their statue finished in time for the anniversary, but the right hand and torch is completed and shown in Philadelphia and New York.

1878

The head and shoulders of the statue are displayed in Paris.

1881

Gustave Eiffel is commissioned to design the statue's inner framework.

Timeline

1884

The statue is constructed in the courtyard of Bartholdi's workshop in Paris. It draws crowds.

1884

Émile Nouguier and Maurice Koechlin, two engineers working for Gustav Eiffel, come up with the idea of a large tower to be the centrepiece of the Exposition Universelle in five years' time.

Timeline

1885

The dismantled Statue of Liberty is shipped to New York.

1886

The Statue of Liberty is constructed on its pedestal on Bedloe's Island, New York, and unveiled to the public.

1886

Édouard Lockroy, the French Minister of Commerce and Industry, announces that the Eiffel Tower will be built in time for the exposition.

1887

Construction of the Eiffel Tower begins in the Champ de Mars, Paris.

Timeline

1888

The first and second levels of the Eiffel Tower are completed. A group of artists, composers and poets protest against it.

1889

The Eiffel Tower opens as part of the Exposition Universelle and is incredibly popular. Almost two million people visit during the first few months.

1923

Gustave Eiffel dies in Paris, France.

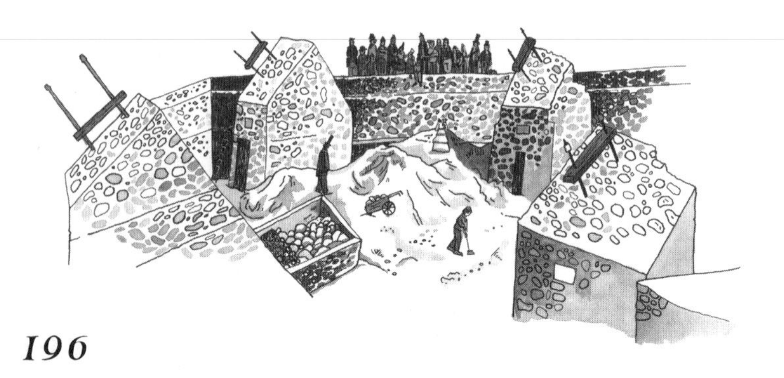

Engineering Hall of Fame

Archimedes
(c.287 BC–c. 212 BC)
The great ancient Greek mathematician was also an important forefather of engineering. He is said to have invented a screw that could pump water, a crane-like claw that could lift enemy ships out of the water, and a system of pulleys for lifting heavy objects.

Engineering Hall of Fame

Elon Musk (1971–)

The most famous engineer of our current age, Musk was raised in South Africa before moving to Canada. He has founded businesses such as Tesla Motors, which makes electric cars, and SpaceX, which became the first private company to send humans to the International Space Station in 2020.

Emily Warren Roebling (1843–1903)

American engineer who became a pioneer for women in the industry. Her husband, Washington Roebling, was the chief engineer on the Brooklyn Bridge, New York, and when he fell ill, she took over. She developed an extensive knowledge of the subject, and guided the bridge to completion in 1883.

Engineering Hall of Fame

Fazlur Rahman Khan
(1929–1982)

Born in Dhaka, which is now part of Bangladesh, Khan studied engineering in India, and became a key figure in skyscraper construction. He pioneered the 'tube structure' for high-rises, which helps them to withstand high winds and earthquakes. He was the designer of Chicago's Sears Tower, which was the tallest building in the world when it opened in 1973.

George Stephenson
(1781–1848)

British engineer known as the 'father of the railways'. He built the locomotive for the first steam-powered passenger railway in 1825. His famous 'rocket' design followed four years later, and ran from Manchester to Liverpool.

Engineering Hall of Fame

Gustave Eiffel
(1832–1923)

French engineer who made his name with railway bridges such as the Garabit Viaduct. He contributed an internal framework to the Statue of Liberty in 1881, but is best remembered for his 300-metre tower. Later in life, he conducted research into air resistance and weather measurement.

Hedy Lamarr
(1914–2000)

Austrian actress, originally called Hedwig Eva Maria Kiesler, who found fame in Hollywood, but also had a passion for invention and engineering. She discovered that the signals of radio-controlled torpedoes in World War II could be jammed and set off course, and designed a 'frequency-hopping' system to keep them safe.

Engineering Hall of Fame

Isambard Kingdom Brunel (1806–1859)

A major figure in the history of engineering, Brunel rose to prominence when helping his father build the Thames Tunnel in London. He designed the Clifton Suspension Bridge across the River Avon, though it was not completed until after his death. And he constructed the vast system of bridges, tunnels and viaducts that became the Great Western Railway, linking London and Bristol.

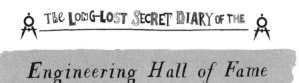

Engineering Hall of Fame

Leonardo da Vinci
(1452–1519)

As well as being the famous artist behind the Mona Lisa, The Last Supper and the Vitruvian Man, da Vinci excelled in many other fields, including engineering. His notebooks show hundreds of inventions, drawn in a detailed style that resembles modern technical drawing.

Nikola Tesla
(1856–1943)

Tesla is widely considered to be one of the greatest inventors of all time. He initially worked for fellow inventor Thomas Edison, before setting up his own laboratory. His engineering background helped him to devise such things as the alternating current motor and the Tesla Coil, the first system that could wirelessly transmit electricity.

Glossary

Arrondissement
A district of a large French city, such as Paris.

Calliper
A measuring device with two hinged legs that resembles a compass.

Cordialement
The French word for 'cordially', which is used to end letters as the equivalent of 'yours sincerely'.

Exposition
A large show in which things such as works of art or pieces of technology are displayed to the public.

Forge
A fire in which metal is heated until it goes soft and can be reshaped.

Foundry
A factory where metal is melted and poured into moulds.

Franc
A monetary unit that was used in France until the introduction of the euro in 2002.

Girder
An iron beam used in the framework of large structures.

Lattice
A structure made from strips of metal that cross each other diagonally.

Glossary

Monsieur
French for 'Mister'.

Mould
A shape made from a material such as wood and metal that is used to produce identical shapes.

Patisserie
A shop where cakes and pastries are sold.

Plinth
The base on which a statue stands.

Pylon
A simple metal tower structure, now commonly used to carry electricity cables.

Republic
A country which is governed by an elected leader rather than a king or queen.

Rivet
A short metal bolt used for permanently fastening two bits of metal together.

Tajine
A traditional North African stew of meat and vegetables named after the shallow dish in which it's cooked.

Vive
'Long live', so for example, 'Vive la France!' means 'Long live France!'

VINS
RETIF
HET

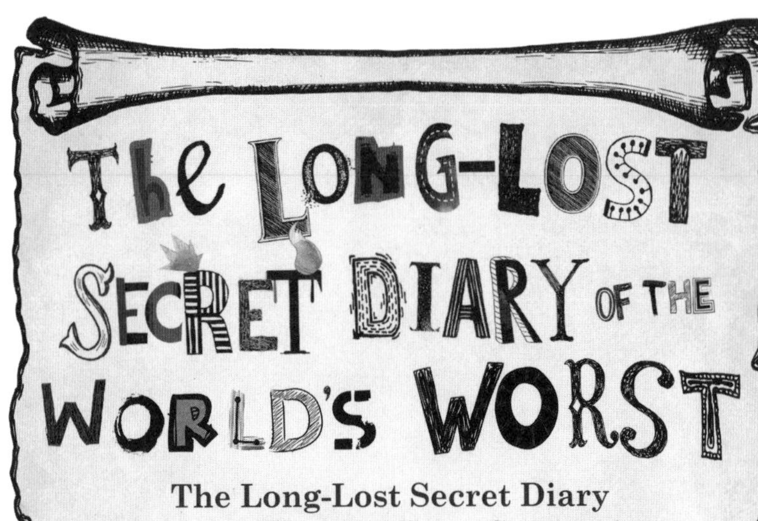
The Long-Lost
Secret Diary of the
World's Worst

The Long-Lost Secret Diary of the World's Worst Samurai
Shortlisted for the 2020–2021 Spark! Kingston and Richmond Children's Book Awards

The Long-Lost Secret Diary of the World's Worst Astronaut
Chosen for the 2019 Summer Reading Challenge.

'Although easy to read, the vocabulary is great and the plot lines engaging – excellent reads for developing readers.'
Library Girl and Book Boy Blog